WORKBOOK 1

NEW

RICHARD HARRISON

ENGLISH PLEASE

PEARSON

Pearson Education Limited
Edinburgh Gate
Harlow
Essex CM20 2JE
England
and Associated Companies throughout the World

www.pearsonlongman.com

First published 2011

20 19 18 17 16 15
IMP   10 9 8 7 6 5

ISBN 9781408272121

Illustrations by Adrian Barclay, Richard Jones and Matt Ward, Beehive Illustration Ltd

Picture research by Frances Topp

Prepared for publication by K and S Design

Printed in Slovakia by Neografia

Contents

Lesson 1 Hello!

 Hello.

 Hello.

 Hello.

1 ● Dictation

Listen and write the names.

a A _ _ B _ _ _ _   d S _ _ _ _ Y _ _ _ _ _

b G _ _ _ K _ _ _   e T _ _ B _ _ _ _

c S _ _ _ _ W _ _ _   f S _ _ _ _ D _ _ _ _ _ _

2 Read and match

a Tom Brown

b Sarah Ward

c John Main

d Sam Smith

e Jane Clark

f Mary Brown

g Ann Barry

1 John Main

2 Mary Brown

3 Jane Clark

4 Ann Barry

5 Tom Brown

6 Sam Smith

7 Sarah Ward

3 Read and write

Read the sentences.

Hello, I'm Ann Jones. Hello, Mrs Jones, I'm Mary Brown.

  capital letters   comma   apostrophe   full stop

Write two more sentences.

Hello, I'm

Hello, I'm

4 Write

Write the names in the lists:

Sarah, Tom, Gary, Ann, John, Sam, Mary, Jane.

Sarah		Tom	

5 Punctuation (' , .?) and capital letters

Write these sentences with punctuation and capital letters.

a   im gary kent

_____

b   how are you

_____

c   fine thanks

_____

d   hello mrs long

_____

6 Write

Complete the greetings.

Example: **I'm Sarah Ward.   Hello, Mrs Ward.**
              I'm Tom Brown.   Hello, Mr Brown.

a   I'm Mary Brown. Hello, _____

b   I'm Sam Smith. _____ , _____

c   I'm Gary Kent. _____

d   I'm Anne Barry. _____

e   I'm Brad Pitt. _____

f   I'm Angelina Jolie. _____

7 **Spelling**

Find and tick (✓) the correct sentence.

Example: How are yo? ☐ How are you? ✓ How ar you? ☐

a Helo, Mrs Long. ☐ Hello, Msr Long. ☐ Hello, Mrs Long. ☐

b How are you? ☐ Hwo are you? ☐ How you? ☐

c I'm fain thnks. ☐ I'm fine thanks. ☐ I'm fine thnks ☐

d Hai Sam! How ar you? ☐ Hai Sam! How you? ☐ Hi Sam! How are you? ☐

Write the correct sentences below.

a _____

b _____

c _____

d _____

8 **Write**

Write these sentences with an apostrophe (').

Example: I am Mary Brown.   I'm Mary Brown.

a I am Leila Al-Rashid. _____

b I am Mohammad Yousef. _____

c I am Lionel Messi. _____

d I am fine thanks. _____

9 **Write**

Write these sentences in the correct order.
a Hello, Mr Kent. I'm Saeed Darwish.
b Fine thanks.
c Hello, I'm Gary Kent.
d How are you, Mr Darwish?

_____

_____

_____

_____

Lesson 2 My name's Bond

1 Group work

Write the names of your group in the table. Ask and answer like this:

What's your name please?   My name's Tawfiq, T-A-W-F-I-Q.

Group _____

1	
2	
3	
4	
5	

2 Write

Practise with other students in the class.

Hello. My name's...   Hello,... . How are you? I'm fine, thank you.

Hello. _____ Sarah Ward.

Hello, Mrs _____ How _____?

_____ you.

3 Spelling

Match the words.

Hello	Helo, Heloo, Hallo, Heelo, Hello
all right	all right, alrght, alrihgt, allright, al right
name	nam, naim, name, nema, naem
please	plis, pleas, pleese, please, plaese
fine	fayn, fain, fine, fane, fien
sorry	sory, sarry, sorry, sorri, sary

4 Punctuation (' , .?) and capital letters

Write these sentences with punctuation and capital letters.

a   my names mohammad yousef

_____

b   how are you

_____

c   mr john main

_____

d   im fine thank you

_____

e   whats your name

_____

f   are you mrs brown

_____

5 Write

Answer the question.

My name's Mohammed Yousef. What's your name?

_____

6 ● Dictation

Listen and write the missing words.

A: Hello.

1 B: _____ your _____ , _____ ?

A: Sarah _____ .

B: W O R D ?

A: No. _____ .

2 A: _____ . _____ Tony Black?

B: _____ . _____ Gary _____ .

A: Oh. _____ _____ Mr Kent.

B: _____ _____ _____ .

7 Write

Write the sentences in full.

I'm sorry. I am sorry.

a I'm fine, thank you.

_____

b My name's Tom.

_____

c What's your name?

_____

d I'm sorry! That's all right.

_____

8 Write

Put the words in the right order.

a are/how/you/? _____

b Mrs Brown/you/are/? _____

c name/is/please/your/what/? _____

Lesson 3 This is Ahmed

1 **Write**

Write in the missing words.

2 **Match**

Match the answers with the questions.

3 **Write**

Make two lists from these names.

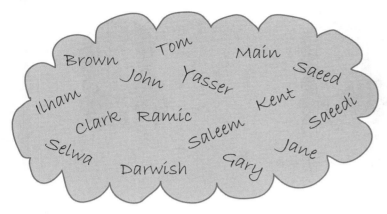

LOOK!

John Main

first name ↗ ↖ family name

Hello, John.

Hello, Mr Main.

First name	Family name
John	Main

4 ● **Listen and write**

Listen to the flight numbers and write them down.

		Flight number
a	London	
b	Paris	
c	Beirut	
d	Tunis	
e	New York	
f	Jeddah	

5 ● **Listen and write**

Write A, B or C below the picture.

☐ ☐ ☐

Now write: **Mrs Brown!** **Mrs Brown?** and **Mrs Brown.**

_____ _____ _____

6 **Write**

Put the words in the right order.

a friend/my/is/this _____

b do/how/you/do? _____

c to/pleased/you/meet _____

d name/is/your/what? _____

e name/Adam/is/my _____

7 **Spelling**

Find the spelling mistakes and correct them. There are 7 mistakes.

a Pleesed to meat you.

_____

b one, tow, three, for, faive

_____

c Hwo do yuo do?

_____

Lesson 4 Good morning

1 Read and write

Good _____ , Sarah. How _____?

I'm _____, thank you. _____?

_____

2 Spelling

Match the words.

friend	frend, frind, freiend, friend, firind
pleased	peleased, pleased, plesed, pleesed, pleazed
morning	mrning, moring, mornning, morning, mourning
afternoon	afternon, afternoon, aftrnoon, aftrenoon, afeternoon
evening	evening, evning, ivening, evenning, eevning
night	night, nihgt, nigth, naight, nght

3 Write

Write the answer.

a Good morning. _____

b How are you? _____

c How do you do? _____

d What's your name? _____

e Are you Mr Darwish? _____

4 **Group work**

Write down the names and telephone numbers of the people in your group.
What's your name?
What's your number?

Group _____

a _____

b _____

c _____

d _____

e _____

5 **Numbers**

Write these numbers.

0 _____ .   1 _____ .   2 _____ .

3 _____ .   4 _____ .   5 _____ .

6 _____ .   7 _____ .   8 _____ .

9 _____ .   10 _____ .

6 **Write**

Write **is ('s), am ('m)** or **are** in the spaces.

a   What _____ your name?   d   This _____ my friend, Adam.

b   How _____ you?   e   I _____ fine, thank you.

c   I _____ pleased to meet you.   f   _____ you Mrs Brown?

7 ◉ Dictation

Listen and write the missing words.

1 A: _____ _____ , Mr Kent.

B: _____ _____ , Ahmed. _____?

A: I'm _____ . _____?

B: _____ .

2 A: _____ _____ . _____ Electronics.

B: _____ . Is that 968 _____?

A: No this is 968 _____ .

B: Oh, _____ .

8 Crossword

Down ↓
1 How are you? I'm ..., thank you.
2 Yes and ... .
3 I'm sorry! That's all ... .
4 Hi!
7 I'm Tom Brown. Hello... Brown.
9 .... two, three, four
10 four, five ... seven
11 Are ... Mrs Brown?

Across →
1 This is my ..., Ahmed.
5 My name ... Selwa.
6 morning, afternoon, ... night
8 Pleased ... to meet you.
10 "Mr Main?"
   "No, I'm Mr Brown."
   "Oh, I'm ..."
12 two, three ..., five

Lesson 1 Who's that?

1 Write

Write the words in the spaces.

_____ that?

I don't know.

_____ Simon Star!

2 Ask and answer

Who's that?   That's ...
I don't know.

 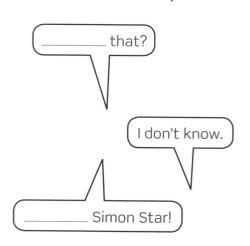   

3 Spelling

Match the words.

mother	mother, mothr, mather, mothre, moter
brother	brather, brother, borther, brohter, berother
daughter	dautgher, daugther, doghter, daghter, daughter
grandfather	granfarther, granfather, grandfther, grandfather, grandfathr
sister	siseter, sisster, sester, saster, sister
nice	nice, naice, niyc, niec, neic
handsome	hansome, hamsome, handsom, hendsome, handsome

4 Match

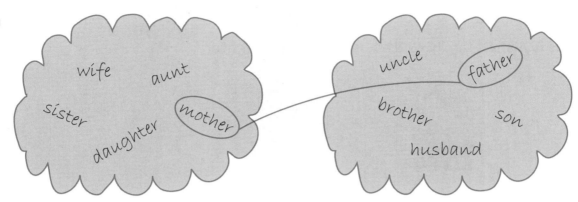

5 Punctuation (' , .?) and capital letters

Write these sentences with punctuation and capital letters.

a   his names ahmed
b   im tom brown
c   this is my wife sarah
d   ali is very handsome
e   my names tawfiq
f   whats her name

6 Write

Write **my, your**, **his** and **her** in the dialogue.

A: Good morning.

A: What's _____ name please?

A: Is this _____ wife, Mr Brown?

A: Mary Brown?

A: And who's this?

B: Good morning.

B: _____ name's Tom Brown.

B: Yes. _____ name's Mary.

B: Yes. That's right.

B: That's _____ son. _____ name's Robert.

7 **Write**

This is Aisha's family. Write **husband**, **son**, **daughter**.

8 **Write**

Complete the dialogues with: **he, she, his** or **her**.

1 A: That's my uncle.

   B: What's _____ name?

   A: Brian.

   B: _____'s handsome.

2 A: That's my daughter.

   B: What's _____ name?

   A: Sue.

   A: _____'s nice.

3 A: And that's my sister.

   B: What's _____ name?

   A: Jenny.

   B: _____'s nice too.

4 A: And that's my young brother.

   B: What's _____ name?

   A: Joe.

   B: _____'s very handsome.

Lesson 2 Good Luck Hotel

1 Write

Write in the words.

2 Write

Write these sentences in the full form.

Example: **It's** expensive.   **It is** expensive.

a   I'm seven and a half.   _____

b   My sister's very nice.   _____

c   His name's Tom.   _____

d   I'm pleased to meet you.   _____

e   Who's that?   _____

f   What's your name?   _____

3 Spelling

Write in the missing vowels: **a, e, i, o, u.**

a   ch _ _ p

b   _ xp _ ns _ v _

c   n _ m _

d   pl _ _ s _ d

e   y _ _ n g

f   h _ t _ l

g   br _ th _ r

4 Numbers

Write these numbers.

11 _____

12 _____

13 _____

14 _____

15 _____

5 Ask and answer

How old is ...?   He's ...
                   She's ...

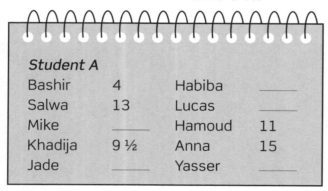

Student A			
Bashir	4	Habiba	_____
Salwa	13	Lucas	_____
Mike	_____	Hamoud	11
Khadija	9 ½	Anna	15
Jade	_____	Yasser	_____

Student B			
Bashir	_____	Habiba	6 ½
Salwa	_____	Lucas	14
Mike	10	Hamoud	_____
Khadija	_____	Anna	_____
Jade	5	Yasser	12

How old are you? _____

6 Write

Write **I**, **you**, **he**, **she**, **it** in the spaces.

a   Hello. How are _____?

b   This is my daughter. _____ is ten years old.

c   My name's Khalid. _____ am pleased to meet you.

d   That is the Good Luck Hotel. _____ is cheap.

e   Are _____ Tom Brown? Yes, that's right.

f   This is my uncle. _____ is very nice.

7 **Write**

Answer the questions.

Is the car new? No. <u>It is old</u> .

a Is the hotel cheap? No. It is _____ .

b Is Tony old? No. He is _____ .

c Is Mariam short? No. _____ .

d Is your brother big? No. _____ .

e Is the car very bad? No. _____ .

f Is your sister young? No. _____ .

8 **Spelling**

Find the spelling mistakes and correct them. There are 10 mistakes.
a His brather is fiften.

_____

b Ali is vary yung.

_____

c My daugther is elven.

_____

d The hotle is very expansive.

_____

e Tom is eigth and a halef.

_____

9 ⦿ **Dictation**

Write the numbers you hear.
Example: 7½,   14,   9834009

a _____

b _____

c _____

d _____

e _____

f _____

g _____

h _____

i _____

j _____

Lesson 3 Where are you from?

1 Countries

Write in the vowels **a**, **e**, **i**, **o**, **u**.

a S _ _ d _ _ r _ b _ _

b _ m _ n

c T _ n _ s _ a

d _ l g _ r _ _

e K _ w _ _ t

f _ m _ r _ c _

2 Questions

Put the words in the right order.

a you/from/are/where/? _____

b you/are/how/? _____

c old/you/how/are/? _____

d America/you/are/from/? _____

e please/what/name/is/your/? _____

3 Match

Match the questions with the answers.

a Where are you from?

b How are you?

c Are you from England?

d How old are you?

1 I'm 18.

2 Not bad, thanks.

3 Yes, from London.

4 From Cairo.

4 Write

Write **who**, **what** or **where** in the dialogue.

A: _____'s that?
B: That's my friend, Steve.

A: Oh. _____'s he from?
B: From Glasgow.

A: Glasgow? _____'s that?
B: In Scotland.

A: And _____'s that?
B: That's his hotel.

5 Read

Match the people with the countries. Write the names on the map.

1   My name's Latifa Al-Rashid. I'm from Sur in Oman.

2   I'm Mohammed. I'm from Tunisia.

3   My name's Ahmed Mansour. I'm from Muharraq in Bahrain.

4   I'm Samia. I'm from Rabat in Morocco.

5   My name's Fahad. I'm from Aswan in Egypt.

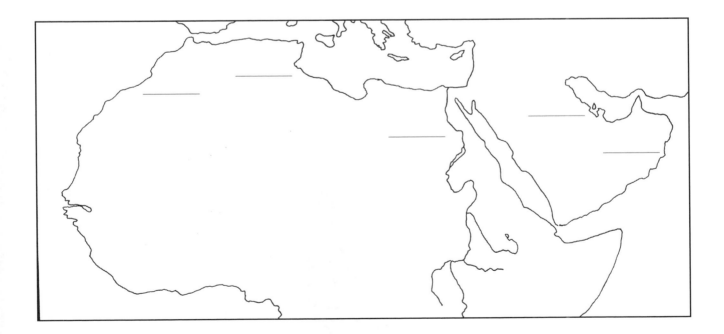

6 Write

Read this sentence again:

My name's Latifa Al-Rashid. I'm from Sur in Oman.

Now write about yourself.

What's your name?

_____

Where are you from?

_____

Now write about five people.

My friend Suzie is from Hong Kong.
Salah is from Mosul in Iraq.

a _____

b _____

c _____

d _____

e _____

7 ● Dictation

Listen and write the missing words.

A: Hello. _____ Sonia.

B: Hi, Sonia. _____ _____ Maria.

A: _____ _____ _____ _____ , Maria?

B: _____ _____ Rome in Italy. _____ _____?

A: _____ _____ Aleppo.

B: _____ that?

A: _____ _____ Syria.

Lesson 4 Welcome!

1 Ask and answer

| What's your name, please? | How do you spell that? |
| Where are you from? | What's your passport number? |

You   *Your Partner*

Name: _____

City: _____

Country: _____

Passport No: _____

<<<<<<<<<<<<<<<<<<<<<<<<<<<<<<<<

Name: _____

City: _____

Country: _____

Passport No: _____

<<<<<<<<<<<<<<<<<<<<<<<<<<<<<<<<

Name: _____

City: _____

Country: _____

Passport No: _____

<<<<<<<<<<<<<<<<<<<<<<<<<<<<<<<<

Name: _____

City: _____

Country: _____

Passport No: _____

<<<<<<<<<<<<<<<<<<<<<<<<<<<<<<<<

2 Spelling

Match the words.

welcome	wellcom, wellcome, wilcome, welcome, willcom
police	polis, bleas, police, polise, plice
passport	pasport, passport, paseport, pusporet, bassport
where	wher, were, wheer, where, ware
spell	spel, spell, espell, speel, speil
England	Engeland, Englnd, Engaland, Ingland, England

3 Look

Find the odd one out.

> a mother, sister, wife, uncle, daughter, aunt.
>
> b father, son, friend, cousin, sister, grandmother.
>
> c handsome, tall, nice, hotel, good, small, bad.
>
> d nineteen, eight, twelve, eleven, number, four, thirteen.
>
> e it, my, you, I, he, she.

4 Punctuation (' , . ?) and capital letters

Write these sentences with capital letters and punctuation.

a hassan is from egypt

_____

b mrs brown is from england

_____

c sousse is in tunisia

_____

d fawzia is from rabat in morocco

_____

e sam smith is from dallas in texas

_____

f wheres tom brown from

_____

5 Write

Write the words in the spaces.

A: What _____ your name please?
B: Sam Smith.

A: _____ to Abu Dhabi, Mr Smith.
B: Thanks.

A: How do _____ spell your family name?
B: S-M-I-T-H

A: _____ are you _____?
B: I _____ from the United States of America.

A: _____ you from New York?
B: No, I'm _____ . I'm from Dallas _____ Texas.

6 Crossword

6 GOOD ... HOTEL.
7 Hello! ...
9 This is my friend, Ahmed. ... is from Saudi Arabia.
11 Who's that. He's handsome. Thank you. That's ...!
12 Father and ... .

Down ↓
1 ... and pull.
2 How do you ... your name?
3

4 seven + five =
8 Hello . ... Tom Brown. (1,2)
9 This is my daughter. ... name is Alia.
10 This is my car. ... is new.
11 Excuse ... . Where are you from?

Across →
1

5 This is my aunt. ... is from Bahrain.

7 Write

Write these sentences in the correct order.
a Mrs Jane Morrison – M O R R I S O N
b No, I'm not. I'm from LA – Los Angeles.
c Where are you from Mrs Morrison?
d What's your name, please?
e I'm from the USA
f Are you from New York?

3 Jobs and nationalities

Lesson 1 He's a mechanic

1 Read

This is my husband, John. He's a policeman. This is my daughter. She's a student.

My name's Fahad. I'm from Sharjah in the United Arab Emirates. I'm a doctor. This is my new car.

2 Write

My name's Nora. I'm from Latakia in Syria. I'm a teacher.

What about you?

My _____

3 Spelling

Match the words.

teacher   techer, teechr, teacher, teachre, ticher, teachr

student   student, studient, stedent, sudent, studunt

doctor   dactor, doctor, docter, dactr, doceter

policeman pliceman, boliceman, poleesman, poliseman, policeman

nurse   nurse, narse, nairse, nurce, nares

woman   wimin, woeman, woman, wommen, women

girl   garl, girl, girel, gairl, gril

4 **Write**

Write sentences like this:

She's a nurse.
No, she isn't a nurse.
She's a doctor.

a   He's a mechanic.

No, _____ .

He's _____ .

c   She's a student.

No, _____ .

She's _____ .

b   You're a taxi driver.

No, _____ .

I'm _____ .

d   I'm a policeman.

No, _____ .

You're _____ .

5 Write

Write the words **your, a, from, are** in the spaces.

A: Where _____ you from?

B: I'm _____ Dammam in Saudi Arabia.

A: What's _____ job?

B: I'm _____ driver for ARAMCO.

6 Write

Write the words **a, isn't, her, aunt, who, is** in the spaces.

A: _____'s that?

B: That's my _____ .

A: What's _____ name?

B: Caroline.

A: _____ she a teacher?

B: No, she _____ . She's _____ nurse.

7 Punctuation (' , .?) and capital letters

Write these sentences with punctuation and capital letters.

a	are you a doctor
b	whats your job
c	i dont have a job
d	he isnt a mechanic
e	youre not a nurse
f	is she a teacher
g	im not a driver

Lesson 2 These are my brothers

1 Write

Complete the chart.

friend	friends	uncle	
cousin		aunt	
son		sister	
daughter		brother	

Now write sentences.

This **is** my friend.
These **are** my friends.

a

c

b

d

2 Spelling

Write **a, e, i, o, u** in these words:

a t _ _ c h _ r

b p _ l _ t

c t h _ s _

d m _ c h _ n _ c

e s t _ d _ n t

f f r _ _ n d

g n _ r s _

h s c h _ _ l

3 Write

Write **is** or **are** in the spaces.

a This _____ my car.

b Mariam _____ a teacher at the Capital English School.

c These _____ my friends.

d Mr and Mrs Brown _____ from England.

e He _____ a driver.

f They _____ mechanics.

4 Write

Write sentences.

He's/She's a student.
They're students.

a

She's a teacher.

b

_____

c

d

e

f

5 🔘 **Listen and write**

a _____

b _____

c _____

6 **Punctuation (, . ' ?) and capital letters**

Write these sentences with punctuation and capital letters.

a	theyre from saudi arabia
b	i dont understand
c	where are you from
d	are they pilots
e	these are my daughters samira and fawzia

Lesson 3 Are you English?

1 **Read and write**

My friend is a doctor. His name is Oscar Mayhew and he is 25 years old. He is from Oxford in England, but he's not English. He's Scottish.

My cousin is from Manama in Bahrain. Her name is Suhair and she is Bahraini. She is a teacher in a secondary school. She is 29.

Tawfiq is Palestinian. He's 22 years old and he is a teacher at a school. He is from Nablus.

Fawzia is 18 years old and she is from Tanta in Egypt. She is Egyptian. She is a student.

Name	Age	Job	Nationality
Oscar Mayhew	25	doctor	Scottish
Suhair			
Tawfiq			
Fawzia			

2 **Write**

Join the sentences with and.

His name is Abdul Qader. He is 25 years old.

His name is Abdul Qader **and** he is 25 years old.

a   Suhair is a teacher in a secondary school. She is 29 years old.

_____

b   My husband is from Alexandria in Egypt. He is a policeman.

_____

c   Ali and Lutfi are from Jeddah. They are students.

_____

d   My cousin is from Morocco. He is a doctor.

_____

3 🔘 **Listen**

Complete the form.

Name: _____

City: _____

Country: _____

Nationality: _____

4 **Write**

Write **I, you, he, she, it, we, they** in the spaces.

a   My friend, Yousef, is from Aleppo. _____ is Syrian.

b   This is my cousin, Samira. _____ is Tunisian.

c   My husband and I are from Algiers. _____ are Algerian.

d   This is my car. _____ is a Toyota.

e   These are my friends, Bahir and Jamal. _____ are students.

f   My name's Ali. _____ am Bahraini.

g   Are _____ Egyptian? Yes, I'm from Cairo.

5 **Ask and answer**

Choose a country and a nationality.

A	B
Where are you from?	I'm from ...
Are you ...?	Yes, I am.
No, I'm not. I'm ...	

6 **Write**

Write the words **am, in, a, from, is, is** in the spaces.

My name _____ Ben. I _____ 26 years old. I am _____ Madrid _____

Spain. I am _____ taxi-driver. My nationality _____ Spanish.

Now write a paragraph about yourself.

7 Word Puzzle

Find and write 10 more nationalities.

H	S	U	D	A	N	E	S	E	F
O	I	R	A	Q	I	B	A	L	R
E	L	E	B	A	N	E	S	E	E
M	D	G	O	T	A	L	Y	U	N
I	U	Y	X	A	T	O	R	I	C
R	T	P	B	R	I	T	I	S	H
A	C	T	U	I	M	J	A	L	K
T	H	I	D	O	M	A	N	I	R
I	B	A	L	G	E	R	I	A	N
E	O	N	S	A	U	D	I	K	V

1 _Sudanese_ _____
2 _____
3 _____
4 _____
5 _____
6 _____
7 _____
8 _____
9 _____
10 _____
11 _____

8 ● Listen and write the missing words

A: _____ _____ _____ _____ , please?

B: _____ _____ Amsterdam in Holland.

A: _____ _____ Dutch?

B: I'm Dutch, _____ _____ _____ _____ from France.

A: _____ _____ ?

B: Yes_____ _____ .

9 Spelling

Find the spelling mistakes and correct them. There are 10 mistakes.

a   Her husbend is twenty-nine yaers olde.

_____

b   Jane is Britsh but her husbnd is Lebnese.

_____

c   Mona is Egyptan ad she is a teaher.

_____

Lesson 4 Where are we?

1 Write

Match with the pictures.

① I'm very sorry.   ② So am I.   ③ Am I late?

2 Write

Complete the sentences with **cold, thirsty, hungry, tired**.

a I'm _____ . Have my jacket.

b I'm _____ . Have a sandwich.

c We're _____ . Have a rest on this seat.

d We're _____ . Have some water.

3 Write

Complete the sentences.

(Sam/cold) **Sam isn't cold** . He's hot.

a (Jane/thirsty) Jane _____ . She's hungry.

b (We/French) _____ . We're Turkish.

c (The car/expensive) _____ . It's cheap.

d (The students/from Spain) _____ . They're from Italy.

37

4 Write

Use these words, I am, You are, He is, She is, It is, We are, You are, They are.

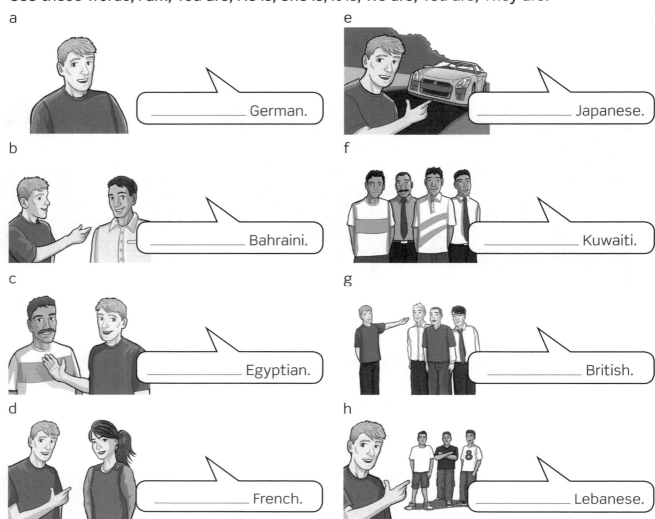

a

_____ German.

e

_____ Japanese.

b

_____ Bahraini.

f

_____ Kuwaiti.

c

_____ Egyptian.

g

_____ British.

d

_____ French.

h

_____ Lebanese.

5 Numbers

Write these numbers.

21 _____

22 _____

23 _____

24 _____

25 _____

26 _____

27 _____

28 _____

29 _____

30 _____

6 ● Listen and draw

Follow the numbers.

```
1    2    3    4    5    6    7
•    •    •    •    •    •    •

8    9   10   11   12   13   14
•    •    •    •    •    •    •

15   16   17   18   19   20   21
•    •    •    •    •    •    •

22   23   24   25   26   27   28
•    •    •    •    •    •    •
```

It's a _____ .

7 Write

Find the jobs.

a	chatree	_____
b	naihccem	_____
c	lopit	_____
d	srenu	_____
e	odtroc	_____
f	ridevr	_____

8 Punctuation (, . ' ?) and capital letters

Write these sentences with punctuation and capital letters.

my names abdul rahim im from abu dhabi im 26 years old and im a clerk

_____

9 Crossword

Down ↓

2 They are …

3 They are from Sousse. They are … .
5 We are cold … hungry.
8 Welcome to my hotel. … is very good.

Across →

1

4 She's from Manama. She's … .

6

7 Sharjah is … Dubai.

9 "I … late."
10 My sister … a nurse.
11 six + four =

4 In the city

Lesson 1 What's that?

1 Write

It's a bank. It's beautiful.
It's a beautiful bank.

a It's a car. It's new. It's a _____

b It's a palace. It's big. _____

c It's a building. It's tall. _____

d It's a hotel. It's cheap. _____

e It's a school. It's very good. _____

2 Write

Write sentences from the words like the examples below.

old / car   It's an old car.
new / camera   It's a new camera.

a tall / building   _____

b beautiful / palace   _____

c expensive / car   _____

d nice / hotel   _____

e new / bank   _____

f old / house   _____

3 Spelling

Match the words.

building	bilding, biulding, building, buildig, bulding
palace	place, balace, palase, pelace, palace
hotel	hotal, hotle, hotell, otel, hotel
school	shool, shcool, schol, sekool, school
bank	bank, banek, bunk, pank, banc
hospital	pospitl, hospitle, haspital, hopsital, hospital
house	hous, hause, house, huse, howse

4 Write

It isn't a man. It's a tree.

It's a man.

a

It's a camera. It isn't _____ . It's _____ .

b

It's a watch. It isn't _____ . It's _____ .

c

It's a car. _____ . _____ .

d

It's a bag. _____ . _____ .

e

It's a boy. _____ . _____ .

f

It's a sandwich. _____ . _____ .

5 Write

Complete the signs.

a  R _ C _ P T _ _ N

b L _ F T

c  T _ L _ P H _ N _

d  T _ _ L _ T S

e  P _ S H

f  P _ L L

g  _ X C H _ N G _

h  N _ SM _ K _ N G

i _ M M _ G R _ T _ _ N

6 Read and match

1 This is a new hotel. It's the Grand Hotel in Leeds. It's near the city centre.
2 The Capital English School is in Bahrain. It is a small school and it is in the centre of the city.
3 This is my hotel – the Good Luck Hotel. It's a nice hotel. It isn't very big, but it's cheap and it's clean.
4 The Global bank is a very big bank. It is near the park in the centre of London.

A

☐

C

☐

B

☐

D

☐

7 ● Dictation

Listen and write the missing words.

A: _____ _____ _____ Amanda?

B: _____ _____ _____ .

Hyde Park.

A: _____ _____ _____ .

And _____ _____

building _____ ?

B: _____ _____ Crown Hotel. It's _____ _____

_____ _____ .

A: And _____ _____ here - near _____ _____ .

Is _____ _____ _____ _____ ?

B: _____ _____ _____ . I think _____

_____ _____ .

Lesson 2 Is it far?

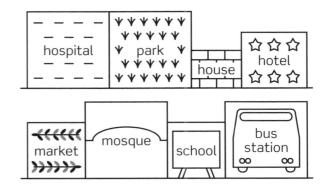

1 Write

Use the table to write the sentences.

The mosque	is near	the bus station.
The school		the market.

a The mosque is near the school.

b _____

c _____

d _____

e _____

2 Questions

Put the words in order.

a hospital / is / where / the / ? _____

b nationality / what / your / is / ? _____

c old / are / you / how / ? _____

d number / is / your / what / telephone / ? _____

e do / that / spell / you / how / ? _____

f books / are / where / my / ? _____

3 Write

Write **a, an, the, (-)** in the spaces.

a It's _____ expensive camera.

b They're _____ old houses.

c He's _____ big man.

d She's _____ old woman.

e It's _____ Capital English School.

f It's _____ tall building.

g It's _____ Tower of London.

h They're _____ expensive hotels.

4 Write

Write these sentences in the right order:

a   The Green Hotel.

b   Pardon?

c   No, not far. It's about a kilometre.

d   Excuse me, where's the Green Hotel?

e   It's near the bus station.

f   Is it far?

_____

_____

_____

_____

_____

_____

5 Write

Write **in, from, to** in the space.

a   Mariam is _____ Algiers. She's Algerian.

b   The mosque is next _____ the park.

c   We're _____ Aleppo _____ Syria.

d   The airport is not far _____ the city.

e   The Taj Mahal is _____ India.

Excuse me, where's the airport?

Pardon?

6 Punctuation (' , . ?) and capital letters

Write out these sentences with punctuation and capital letters.

a whats that

_____

b its my new car

_____

c thats the sheraton hotel

_____

d is that the bank of oman

_____

e were near the school

_____

7 ● Dictation

Write the numbers you hear in these sentences.

a _____ f _____

b _____ g _____

c _____ h _____

d _____ i _____

e _____ j _____

8 ● Dictation

Listen and write the missing words.

A: Excuse me, _____ _____

_____?

B: _____ _____

_____ _____ _____-station.

A: _____ _____ _____?

B: _____ _____ _____ kilometres.

4

Lesson 3 The market

1 Write

This apple	is	sweet. good. bad. nice. cheap. expensive.
These oranges	are	

a dates / sweet   These _____

b watermelon / bad This _____

c lemons / cheap   _____

d bananas / good   _____

e apple / nice   _____

f oranges / expensive _____

2 Look

Find the word that is different:

a school, hotel, mosque, park, airport, palace, hospital

b apple, orange, fruit, banana, watermelon, lemon

c teacher, doctor, nurse, job, secretary, driver, mechanic

d who, where, how, that, what

e thirsty, hungry, tired, sandwich, cold, happy, hot

f Qatar, Saudi Arabia, Egyptian, Jordan, Tunisia, Yemen

3 Numbers

Write the numbers.

35 _____   58 _____

39 _____   59 _____

46 _____   60 _____

48 _____   63 _____

51 _____   67 _____

4 Match

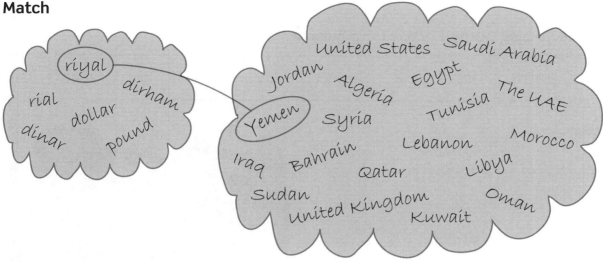

5 Write

They're dates. They're sweet. They're sweet dates.

a They're houses. They're old.

   They're _____

b They're watches. They're expensive.

   They're _____

c They're new. They're drivers.

   _____

d They're doctors. They're very good.

   _____

e They're apricots. They're Egyptian.

   _____

6 Read

Ask and answer.

How much are the dates?
How much are … ?

They're 20 dirhams a kilo.
They're …

7 **Write**

Write the missing words. Choose from these words:

> are   Jordan   it's   what   sweet   kilo   those   half   that   much

A: What's _____?

B: _____ a melon.

A: Is it _____?

B: Yes very sweet. It's from _____ .

A: And _____ are _____?

B: They _____ Kiwi fruits.

A: How _____ are they?

B: One pound for one _____ .

A: _____ a kilo please.

8 **Spelling**

Find the spelling mistakes and correct them. There are ten mistakes.

a How mach are the aples?

_____

b The daites are from Tuinsia

_____

c What are thees? Are they limons?

_____

d Five killos of bannas, please.

_____

e I'm sarry. I don't now.

_____

9 **Match the questions and the answers**

a What are those?   1 It's a digital camera.
b How much is this TV?   2 They are apricots.
c What is that?   3 It's 55 dinars.
d How much are the oranges?   4 One dinar for two kilos.
e Are they sweet?   5 Yes, they are.

Lesson 4 Streets and roads

1 Write

Is _____ the _____ to Jeddah?

No, _____ _____ . This is the _____ _____ _____ .

Is _____ Liberty _____ ?

_____'s the Capital English _____ ?

Yes, that's _____ .

It's _____ .

2 Spelling

Match the words.

station	staiton, station, staytion, stashon, staition
garage	garage, grage, garag, gahage, garíje
problem	broblem, probelem, prablem, broplem, problem
orange	orinҳe, orange, orinj, ornge, ornige
street	streat, street, stret, stíreet, straet
road	rode, road, raod, roade, rood
petrol	peterol, betrol, beterel, petríl, petrol

3 Match

Match the words with opposite meanings.

late hot full sour here far

there near empty cold early sweet

4 ● **Listen and say**

□ □   □ □   □ □   □ □
thirteen   thirty   fourteen   forty

Circle the number you hear.

a 13 30   d 16 60
b 14 40   e 17 70
c 15 50   f 19 90

5 ● **Listen**

Circle the numbers.

20	21	22	23	24	25	26	27	28	29
30	31	32	33	34	35	36	37	38	39
40	41	42	43	44	45	46	47	48	49
50	51	52	53	54	55	56	57	58	59
60	61	62	63	64	65	66	67	68	69
70	71	72	73	74	75	76	77	78	79
80	81	82	83	84	85	86	87	88	89
90	91	92	93	94	95	96	97	98	99

6 **Numbers**

Write these numbers:

71 _____   89 _____

74 _____   92 _____

76 _____   93 _____

85 _____   97 _____

88 _____   100 _____

7 **Punctuation (' , .?) and capital letters**

Write these sentences with punctuation and capital letters.

the capital english school is in liberty street it is not far from the market next to the school is a new bank the bank of the arabian gulf

8 Crossword

[crossword grid]

Across →

1

3 Where's ... market?
4 nine + five = ...
6 This is ... new car.

7

9 Your grandfather is very ... .

Down ↓

1 thirty-three + seventeen =
2

3 Who's that? Who? That man, ...
5 She's a ... .

6 He's a ... .

8 How much ... this jacket?
10 I'm hungry. Have ... apple.
11 How ... you spell your name?
12 Excuse ..., where's the Meridian Hotel?

5 What's it like?

Lesson 1 That's mine!

1 Write

Write **my**, **your**, **his**, **her**, **our**, **their** in the spaces.

What's _____ name, please?

I'm Tom Brown.

These are my friends, Ahmed and Samia, and this is _____ daughter.

What's _____ name?

Muna.

This is my son. _____ name's Tawfiq.

Is this _____ room?

Yes, that's right.

Where's _____ passport?

2 Spelling

Match the words.

black	blick, belack, bleck, black, balck
red	rid, red, raid, read, reed
white	wite, white, wait, whiyet, whyt
blue	bleu, belu, blue, below, blew
brown	brawn, barown, browen, brown, brewn
green	grin, gren, grean, green, gareen
like	laik, lake, laek, like, liyk
mine	mine, main, mien, mane, miyn

3 **Write**

Write **my, mine, your, yours** in the spaces.

A: Excuse me. I think this is _____ seat.

B: No, it isn't. That's _____ seat. There.

A: No. That's _____ This is _____ .

B: Oh. Sorry.

4 **Use the table to complete the sentences.**

A lemon_____ .

Dates _____ _____ .

A watermelon _____ _____ .

Apples _____ _____ or _____ .

Bananas _____ _____ .

An apricot _____ _____ .

A lemon	is	red blue black
Dates	are	green white brown yellow

Now write four sentences with colours about you.
For example: **Our car is black and red. My house is white.**

_____

_____

_____

_____

5 Read and write

My car is five years old.
It's a pick-up.
It's blue and white.

I don't have a car.

My brother's car is new.
It's a white Mercedes.

Our car is a red Datsun.
It's eight years old.

Write about a car. What's it like?

_____

_____

6 Read

Read the advertisements.

FOR SALE
Datsun 1.6 litre.
2007 model. New brakes.
Excellent condition.
Only 20,000 dhms
Telephone : 756-3398

FOR SALE
Mitsubishi pick-up.
Three years old.
Only 3,000 kilometres.
Very good condition.
Price: 2500 JD
Tel : 265-892

A BARGAIN!
A Nissan Patrol for sale.
White and brown.
4-wheel drive.
2005 model.

50,000 km.
Good condition.
Price : OR 1100 o.n.o
Phone Salem 943-543
Ext 65

Now write an advertisement for a car.

_____

_____

_____

_____

_____

Lesson 2 Whose is this?

1 **Write**

_____ ticket is this?

It's _____

2 **Spelling**

Find the colours.

a	lueb _____	e	wonrb _____
b	clabk _____	f	tewih _____
c	owleyl _____	g	dre _____
d	enreg _____		

3 **Spelling**

Find the words. Write: **a, e, i, o, u**.

a w h _ s _

b s _ _ t c _ s _

c t _ c k _ t

d m _ n _ y

e h _ n d b _ g

f r _ _ m

g k _ y s

h p _ s s p _ r t

4 **Write**

Write **they're, there** or **their** in the spaces.

a   Where's my book? It's _____ . Look!

b   Where are Abdullah and Mohammed from? I think _____ from Saudi Arabia.

c   Where are Tom and Mary? They are in _____ room.

5 **Match**

Match the question and the answer.

a (Who is that?)   1 (It's a new bank.)

b (Where's your hotel?)   2 (I'm tired!)

c (How much is that?)   3 (It's my brother's.)

d (What is that?)   4 (39.)

e (How old are you?)   5 (That's my cousin, Bashir.)

f (Whose bike is that?)   6 (Near the market.)

g (How are you?)   7 (Five pounds.)

6 **Punctuation (' , . ?) and capital letters**

Write out these sentences with punctuation and capital letters.

a	whose is that
	_____
b	it isnt mine
	_____
c	its samiras
	_____
d	that's my brothers car
	_____
e	is this yours
	_____
f	theyre ahmeds keys
	_____

7 • **Listen**

Listen to the numbers and cross them out (**X**) as you hear them.

7	11	13	18	19
20	24	29	30	35
44	47	49	52	54
63	66	70	75	78
80	85	90	97	100

One number is not crossed out. What is it?

8 **Read**

Write the names **Bradley, Frazer, Tom** and **Sam** under the doors.

Tom's room is next to Sam's room. Frazer's room is next to Bradley's room, but it isn't near Tom's room. Bradley's room is next to Sam's room and it's next to Frazer's room. It isn't next to Tom's room.

_____   _____   _____   _____

9 **Write**

Write **who, who's** or **whose** in these sentences.

a _____ are you? I'm Sam.

b _____ bag is that near the seat?

c _____ that man in the photo? That's my husband.

d _____ are those boys with the football? They are Tom's sons.

e _____ this girl in the photo? She's my niece, Emma.

f Look at that money on the floor. _____ is it?

Lesson 3 She's got green eyes

1 Write

Sorry _____ late.

It doesn't _____ .

LOOK!

What's the time?
It's ten o'clock.

2 Ask and answer

What's the time?   It's ... o'clock.

   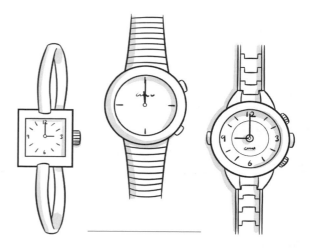

_____   _____   _____

3 Spelling

Match the words.

fair	fare, fair, fiar, fire, fear
grey	grey, griy, garey, girey, grai
quite	quait, quiet, qite, quite, qwite
very	vary, veri, vry, very, vairy
beard	berd, beard, beerd, baerd, bread
moustache	mustache, moustache, mustache, moustach, mostache
thin	then, than, thain, thine, thin
beautiful	beatiful, beautifull, beutiful, beautiful, beatful

4 **Write**

This is my brother. He is tall. **My brother is tall.**

a   This is my son. He is quite tall.

_____

b   This is my sister. She's got brown hair and brown eyes.

_____

c   This is my friend, Ahmed. He has got a beard and a moustache.

_____

d   This is my grandfather. He's got grey hair.

_____

e   This is my daughter. She's eight years old.

_____

5 **Write**

Write in full form.

a   They're from Saudi Arabia. **They are from Saudi Arabia.** _____

b   She's got black hair. _____

c   He isn't thirsty. _____

d   She's a teacher. _____

e   Where's he from? _____

f   He's got a beard. _____

g   What's it like? _____

h   He's a clerk in a bank. _____

i   We aren't from Oman. _____

j   It's a nice hotel. _____

LOOK!

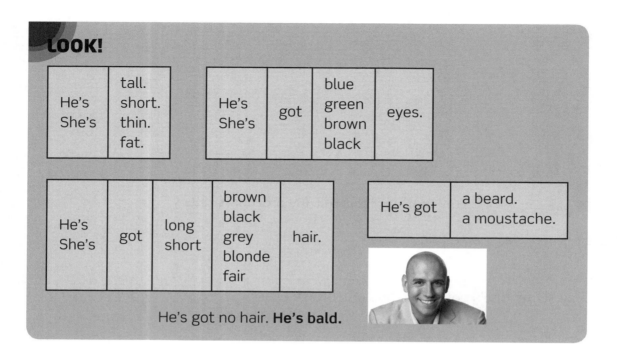

He's She's	tall. short. thin. fat.		He's She's	got	blue green brown black	eyes.

He's She's	got	long short	brown black grey blonde fair	hair.		He's got	a beard. a moustache.

He's got no hair. **He's bald.**

6 **Read and match**

 a

 b

 c

d

1   My aunt's name is Nadia. She's not very tall. She's got long black hair and brown eyes. She's quite old and she's very thin.

_____

2   Peter Roberts is quite tall. He's a teacher in a secondary school in Oman. He's got fair hair and blue eyes. He's got a big moustache, too.

_____

3   My brother's name is Tariq. He's big and quite fat. He's got short black hair and a moustache. He's not very handsome.

_____

4   Ann Hobson is a secretary in a bank. She's quite small and thin. She's got long blonde hair and blue eyes.

_____

7 **Write**

Write about two people you know.

_____

_____

Lesson 4 How many?

1 Write

Write the plurals.

	singular	*plural*	
s	a son a girl a house	son**s** _____ _____	
es	a box a watch a sandwich	box**es** _____ _____	
ies	a baby a country a city	bab**ies** _____ _____	
irregular	a child  a man a woman	_____ men women	

2 How many?

six boxes _____ _____ _____ _____

_____ _____ _____ _____

3 Questions

Put the words in order.

a brother / 's / like / what / your / ?

_____

b many / got / you / children / have / how / ?

_____

c married / you / are / ?

_____

d ticket / this / whose / is / ?

_____

e your / old / daughter / how / is / ?

_____

Now match with the answers.

1 (I haven't got any.)   2 (He's tall and quite handsome.)

3 (It's mine.)   4 (Two and a half.)   5 (No, I'm single.)

4 Spelling

Match the words.

children   childeren, chilidren, children, childrn, childerin

women   wmen, woman, wemen, women, womin

daughter   daughter, dauhgter, duaghter, daughtr, doughter

son   sun, san, son, sen, soon

married   maried, marryed, marred, married, marrid

single   sangle, single, singel, snigle, singal

5 Write

Write these words **a, the, in, got, old, is, is, children** in the spaces.

My friend Khalid _____ from Cairo. He's Egyptian. He's _____ clerk in the

Ministry of Labour. He's _____ a flat in Dokki _____ Cairo. He's got a wife and

two _____ , a boy and a girl. The boy _____ three years old and _____ girl is

eighteen months _____ .

6 Read and write

My friend Samia is Omani. She's a student at the Sultan Qaboos University. She's twenty-three years old. She's married but she hasn't got any children. Her husband is an officer in the army.

Write about a friend.

Where is he/she from? What's his/her job? Is he/she married or single? How many children has he/she got?

My friend _____

_____

_____

_____

7 Crossword

Down ↓
1 Waleed's not tall. He's ... .
2 I'm sorry I'm late. ... doesn't matter.
3

4 twenty-three – seventeen =
6 I'm hungry. Have you ... any dates?
7 Salah's 26 ... old.
8 ... ticket is this? It's mine!
10 Ali's a clerk in the Ministry ... Labour.

Across →

1

5 Tea ... Coffee? Tea, please.
7 The colour of lemons.
9 What's that? It's ... Great Pyramid of Giza.
10 Those are ... seats, not yours!
11

12 "How many children have you got? Three – two daughters and one ...

6 Where is it?

Lesson 1 The second door on the right

1 Write

_____ _____ Ministry of Foreign Affairs, please?

Go _____ this _____ . It's _____ _____ left.

2 Spelling

Match the words.

ground	gruond, garound, ground, graund, geround
first	frist, first, firest, fairst, ferst
second	secand, sckond, scond, seconed, second
third	thaird, third, therd, thired, tird
left	left, lift, laft, lefit, lefft
right	right, raight, rigth, rite, righte
stairs	sters, stiars, stares, stairs, steers
broken	browken, broken, brokin, beroken, brokn
office	office, ofice, offise, offis, offis

3 Match

Go along the corridor. Go up the stairs. Go down the stairs. Stop. Wait.

_____ _____ _____ _____ _____

_____ _____ _____ _____ _____

4 Write

Write **a**, **an**, **the** or **(-)** in the spaces.

a Excuse me. Where's _____ airport?

b What's that building over there?
   It's _____ hotel.

c These are _____ fresh dates.

d It's _____ third door on _____
   right.

e It's _____ beautiful palace.

f They're _____ expensive cars.

g It's _____ old house.

h His office is on _____ fifth floor.

i Hassan's from _____ Morocco.

5 Read and write

Read about ITC. Write these places on the plan:

the canteen, the computer room, the lift, the reception, the manager's office, the toilets, the secretary's office, the stairs, the photocopying room.

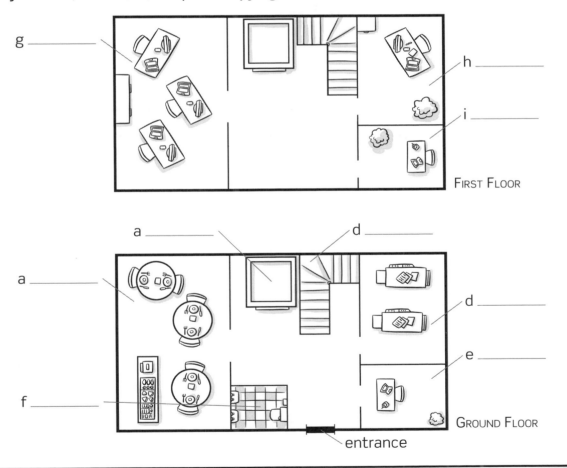

FIRST FLOOR

GROUND FLOOR

entrance

These are the offices of ITC, an engineering company. The reception is on the ground floor next to the entrance, on the right. The photocopying room is also on the right next to the stairs. The lift is next to the stairs. The canteen is on the left next to the lift. The toilets are near the entrance, on the left. The manager's office is on the first floor near the stairs. The secretary's office is a small room. It is next to the manager's office on the right. The computer room is on the left.

6

6 **Ask and answer**

Where's the ...? Where are the ...?	It's They're	on the ... floor. near the ... . next to the ... .

Ask about **the canteen, the reception, the manager's office, the secretary's office, the toilets, the computer room, the stairs, the lift, the photocopying room.**

7 **Write**

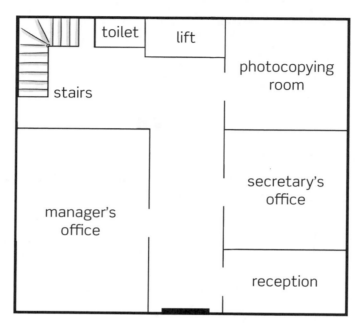

These are the offices of ABC Ltd. The reception is on the right near the entrance.

Lesson 2 Latifa's village

1 Write

_____ there _____ good restaurants near here?

Yes, _____ _____ a nice restaurant _____ to the bus station.

2 Spelling

Spell these rooms. Write **a, e, i, o, u**.

a k _ t c h _ n

b s _ t t _ n g r _ _ m

c b _ d r _ _ m

d cl _ s s r _ _ m

e _ f f _ c _

f t _ _ l _ t

Match with the pictures.

1 _____

2 _____

3 _____

4 _____

5 _____

6 _____

3 Write

Write **on** or **in**.

a   Jeddah is _____ Saudi Arabia.

b   My house is _____ the middle of the village.

c   Her office is _____ the third floor.

d   Tom is a clerk _____ a bank.

e   The photocopying room is _____ the right.

f   The Montazah Palace is _____ Alexandria.

4 Write

Write **am**, **is** or **are**.

a   They _____ from Saudi Arabia.

b   Nadia _____ an English teacher.

c   There _____ two hotels on the right.

d   Whose car _____ this?

e   Where _____ you from?

f   I _____ sorry.

g   There _____ a toilet next to the lift.

h   We _____ hungry. _____ there a restaurant near here?

i   _____ I late?

5 Look and say

1) **Student A.** Write the names of the buildings.

_____   _____   _____

2) **Student B.** Talk about this street.

There is ...   next to ...   There are ...   between ... and   on the left/right.

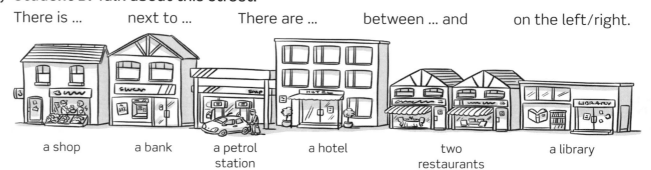

a shop   a bank   a petrol station   a hotel   two restaurants   a library

6 **Write**

There is a bank on _____ left. Next _____ the bank there _____ a restaurant.

On the right _____ is a small _____ . On the _____ of the school there is a

_____ . _____ the garage and the hotel _____ are two small _____ .

Write about this street.

There is a shop on the left. Next to the shop _____

_____

_____

_____

_____

_____

7 **Word puzzle**

Find the places in the city.

Look at the example.
Then find 11 more.

_____bank_____

A	T	M	E	S	H	O	P	B	Z
I	H	O	T	E	L	X	G	A	H
R	E	S	T	A	U	R	A	N	T
P	A	Q	P	B	M	O	R	K	U
O	V	U	A	P	A	L	A	C	E
R	J	E	R	F	K	U	G	A	O
T	A	S	K	E	D	R	E	I	K
B	U	S	S	T	A	T	I	O	N
D	M	I	M	A	R	K	E	T	A
F	H	O	S	P	I	T	A	L	R

_____

_____

_____

_____

_____

Lesson 3 Can I speak to Mrs Roberts?

1 Write

I'm sorry, _____ busy.

ITC

Can I _____ to Mr. James?

2 Write

Put the letters in the correct order.

a DUNSYA _____

b ESDTAUY _____

c DEDSEANWY _____

d NODAMY _____

e AFIDYR _____

f TURSYHDA _____

g SAYAUDRT _____

Now write the days of the week in order.

_____

_____

3 Write

Put the sentences in order.

a His secretary's out.
b OK. I'll phone again this afternoon.
c Can I speak to his secretary?
d Good afternoon. Can I speak to the manager?

e Goodbye.
f Gulf Academy. Good afternoon.
g I'm sorry, he's busy.

1 _____

2 _____

3 _____

4 _____

5 _____

6 _____

7 _____

4 Write

Write these sentences in their full form.

a   He's busy.   _____

b   That's Gary's office.   _____

c   Mary's got three children.   _____

d   I'm not hungry.   _____

e   We're from Syria.   _____

f   I've got a house.   _____

g   She isn't here today.   _____

h   I'll phone again this afternoon.   _____

i   There's a garage on the right.   _____

5 Punctuation and capital letters

Write out these sentences with punctuation and capital letters.

a   tomorrow is saturday

_____

b   go along the corridor

_____

c   where the managers office

_____

d   theres a bank on the right

_____

e   is today sunday or monday

_____

f   can I speak to mrs brown please

_____

6 • **Listen and write**

Listen to the hotel manager. Where are these places?

a small restaurant
b large restaurant
c room 418
d coffee shop
e shops
f reception
g room 235

7 **Questions**

Put the words in the correct order.

a in / days / a week / there / many / are / how ?

_____

b Mrs Darwish / please / I / to / can / speak ?

_____

c orange / I / please / can / an / juice / have ?

_____

d class / there / many / in / students / how / are / the ?

_____

e any / the office / there / near / are / shops ?

_____

f a computer / room / there / in / the / is ?

_____

Now match the questions to these answers:

1 I'm sorry. She's out.
2 There are some on the right, near the school.
3 About 18.
4 There are seven.
5 No, there isn't.
6 Certainly. That's one pound please.

Lesson 4 Peter's classroom

1 Match

Match the prepositions:
up, down, along, next to, near, between, in, on

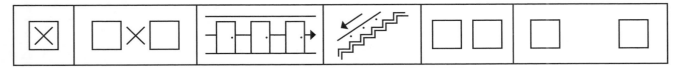

_____ _____ _____ _____ _____ _____

2 Spelling

Double letters. Put the double letters in these words.

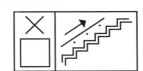

Example: co<u>rr</u>idor

a   s i _ _ i n g room

b   m i _ _ l e

c   o _ _ i c e

d   v i _ _ a g e

e   c l a _ _ r o o m

f   t o m o _ _ o w

g   s o _ _ y

3 Spelling

Match the words.

cupboard	cuboard, cupboard, cubboard, cupbaord, cupbroad
table	taible, taeble, table, tabel, tayble
window	wandow, window, windowe, wndow, waindow
desk	desk, dask, disk, deks, daks
door	doer, door, dore, dower, dare

4 ● Listen and write

Numbers.

387

Now write the numbers in full.

_____ _____ _____ _____

_____ _____ _____ _____

_____ _____ _____ _____

5 Write

Write **in** or **on** in the spaces.

> a   Are there any desks _____ the room?
>
> b   Where's my book? It's _____ the table.
>
> c   There's a house _____ the left.
>
> d   Their flat is _____ the tenth floor.
>
> e   The Statue of Liberty is _____ New York.
>
> f   There's a beautiful park _____ the middle of London.
>
> g   My petrol station is _____ the right.
>
> h   There's a beautiful picture _____ the wall.
>
> i   Where's my passport? It's _____ your handbag.

6 Questions

Put the words in order.

a   you / I / can / help ? _____

b   office / is / Mr Saeedi's / please / where ? _____

c   station / village / in / is / a / there / the / petrol ? _____

d   the / there / room / how / chairs / in / many / are ? _____

e   like / is / house / what / your ? _____

f   speak / Sarah / I / please / can / to ? _____

Now match the answers with the questions:

1   Yes. Just a minute.

2   It's big, but it's very old.

3   No, there isn't. I'm sorry.

4   About 20 I think.

5   Go along the corridor. It's on the right.

6   Yes, please. Where is the reception?

7 **Read and write**

Tom is a teacher at the Capital English School. This is Tom's classroom.

Complete the paragraph.

There are ten desks and chairs in Tom's classroom. On the _____ there _____ a table

with _____ books on it. There _____ two _____ on the wall. The board is on the

middle _____ and next _____ it there is a small _____ . Tom's desk is _____ the

middle of the room. _____ is a CD player on his _____ and a _____ on the left.

On the right there is a large _____ and next to it there _____ a door.

8 **Crossword**

1		2		3		4		5
							6	
7								
							8	
		9			10			11
12				13				
		14				15		
	16					17		
18								

Across →

2   1000 = a ...
6   The traffic light is green. ...!
7

9   My sister and I are from Doha. ... are Qatari.
10 Right or ...?
12 I'm sorry. Mr Jones is ... here.
14 10th

Down ↓

1

2   ... are two airports in the city.
3   Where's the manager's ... please? It's the second room on the right.
4   That's a primary ... .
5

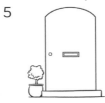

8   There's a table in the middle ... the room.
11 First, second, ...
13 Our flat is ... the sixth floor.
14 Aleppo is in Syria. Damascus is in Syria ... .
15 ... many room are there is this hotel?
16 Where's the lift? Over there. Next ... the stairs.
17 We are from Cairo. ... nationality is Egyptian.
18 Today is Sunday. ... is Monday.

Notes

Notes

notes

Notes